Elements

CARBON

C

Grolier Educational

SHERMAN TURNPIKE, DANBURY, CONNECTICUT 06816

How to use this book

This book has been carefully developed to help you understand the chemistry of the elements. In it you will find a systematic and comprehensive coverage of the basic qualities of each element. Each two-page entry contains information at various levels of technical content and language, along with definitions of useful technical terms, as shown in the thumbnail diagram to the right. There is a comprehensive glossary of technical terms at the back of the book, along with an extensive index, key facts, an explanation of the periodic table, and a description of how to interpret chemical equations.

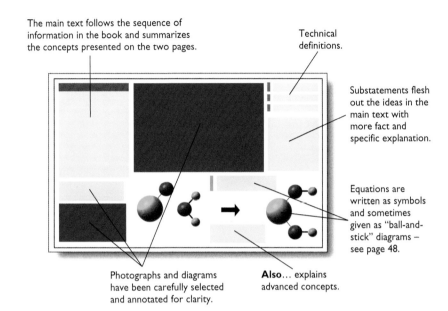

The main text follows the sequence of information in the book and summarizes the concepts presented on the two pages.

Technical definitions.

Substatements flesh out the ideas in the main text with more fact and specific explanation.

Equations are written as symbols and sometimes given as "ball-and-stick" diagrams – see page 48.

Photographs and diagrams have been carefully selected and annotated for clarity.

Also... explains advanced concepts.

Author
Brian Knapp, BSc, PhD
Project consultant
Keith B. Walshaw, MA, BSc, DPhil
         (Head of Chemistry, Leighton Park School)
Industrial consultant
Jack Brettle, BSc, PhD (Chief Research Scientist, Pilkington plc)
Art Director
Duncan McCrae, BSc
Editor
Elizabeth Walker, BA
Special photography
Ian Gledhill
Illustrations
David Woodroffe
Designed and produced by
EARTHSCAPE EDITIONS
Print consultants
Landmark Production Consultants Ltd
Reproduced by
Leo Reprographics
Printed in Hong Kong by
Wing King Tong Company Ltd

First published in the United States in 1996 by Grolier Educational, Sherman Turnpike, Danbury, CT 06816

First reprint 1997, second reprint 1997, and third reprint 2000. New and revised edition 2002

Copyright © 1996 & 2002
Atlantic Europe Publishing Company Limited

Cataloging information may be obtained directly from Grolier Educational.

Volumes 1-18 Set ISBN: 0–7172–5674–X
Volume 8 ISBN: 0–7172–7580–9
Library of Congress Number: 95–082222
Dewey: 546—dc21

Acknowledgments
The publishers would like to thank the following for their kind help and advice: *ICI (UK), Molly and Paul Stratton, Audrey and Teoh Kah Tin, Gutherie Plantation & Agricultural Sdn Bhd and the Kumpulan Gutherie Estate, Catherine and Ian Gledhill, and David Newell.*

Picture credits
All photographs are from the **Earthscape Editions** photolibrary except the following:
(c=center t=top b=bottom l=left r=right)
Courtesy of **ICI(UK)** 26bl and **ZEFA** 41t, 43b.

Front cover: Plastic chips are heated and extruded to make plastic products.
Title page: Adhesives are frequently polymers built from cracked petroleum products.

This product is manufactured from sustainable managed forests. For every tree cut down at least one more is planted.

The demonstrations described or illustrated in this book are not for replication. The Publisher cannot accept any responsibility for any accidents or injuries that may result from conducting the experiments described or illustrated in this book.

Contents

Introduction

An element is a substance that cannot be broken down into a simpler substance by any known means. Each of the 92 naturally occurring elements is therefore one of the fundamental materials from which everything in the Universe is made. This book is about the element carbon.

Carbon

Carbon, the sixth most common element on Earth, is an essential part of nearly all living things. About 94% of the six million known compounds contain carbon, far more than any other element.

Carbon, in the form of diamond, is the hardest natural material on Earth. Carbon is found in a wide variety of rocks, such as chalk and limestone. Compounds of carbon such as coal, natural gas and oil provide the world's most important fuels.

Carbon dioxide gas is one of the main compounds in the air, playing a vital role in controlling the temperature of the atmosphere (it is what we call a "greenhouse gas"). Carbon dioxide is also found dissolved in all water.

Carbon is an essential element in many of the man-made, or synthetic, substances that we use in the modern world, for example, plastics, all synthetic fabrics, many medicines and a wide variety of other chemicals.

Not surprisingly, perhaps, among this huge variety of substances, most of which are good for

our way of living, there are some that cause concern. Carbon-containing compounds called CFCs have been responsible for destroying part of the world's protective ozone layer. Other compounds, such as the pesticide DDT, may be life-threatening if human beings and animals are exposed to them.

Historically, as scientists tried to classify the bewildering array of carbon-based compounds, they made an important distinction between those they called organic compounds and those called inorganic compounds. Limestone rock (calcium carbonate) and carbon gases (such as carbon dioxide and carbon monoxide) are part of the group called inorganic chemicals. Chemicals like those based on petroleum, which are formed from living tissue, are by far the most numerous and are called organic chemicals.

Because carbon compounds so greatly outnumber those made of any other element, it would be impossible to include examples of the majority of the compounds and their properties. Rather, this book will describe the main categories of carbon compounds and a few of the most common compounds.

◀ This is silicon carbide, a compound of silicon and carbon, SiC, whose crystals form black, glossy plates. It is an extremely hard mineral and known by the common name of carborundum. When ground down into a grit, carborundum makes an abrasive that is widely used in industry.

What do carbon compounds have in common?

Carbon is part of many compounds, all of which have certain common properties. For example:

❶ Few carbon based-compounds change quickly at ordinary temperatures, but they begin to react fiercely at high temperatures (as in burning).

❷ All carbon compounds that derive from living tissues — plants, tar, oil, natural gas, etc. — will burn (they are combustible) and can be used as a fuel. When they burn, the compound is oxidized and carbon dioxide is produced. The remaining material is nearly pure carbon (which can be seen in the charred nature of burned wood, for example).

❸ Many carbon-based compounds are not attracted to water and so in general do not dissolve in water. As a result, water alone cannot be used to remove grease or oil from a surface, nor will water dissolve our skin, because all of these things are carbon compounds.

❹ Groups that contain carbon and nitrogen often have an unpleasant smell in liquid form. Some people compare it to rotting fish. Such smells are mainly confined to the factories where the materials are made. The common fabric material nylon, for example, which is a plastic that contains nitrogen, has no smell once it is made into a yarn.

❺ Some compounds of carbon and nitrogen are very unstable and can be made into explosives. Two of the more common explosives are TNT (trinitrotoluene) and nitroglycerine (glycerol trinitrate).

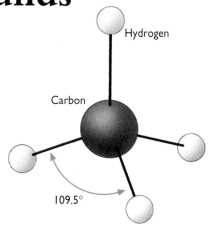

▲ This is a model of a hydrocarbon molecule. It consists of a central carbon atom linked (bonded) to four hydrogen atoms to form the molecule methane (CH_4).

What is so special about carbon?

Carbon is very special because it can form so many compounds. The explanation lies deep inside the atom. Carbon atoms can form strong links with four other atoms. This dramatically increases the number of patterns that carbon atoms can make.

Carbon can also link together in long chains or rings, carbon to carbon to carbon to carbon and so on. Chemists call these links chemical bonds; very long chains, made by joining short ones, are called polymers. And, quite unusually, these long chains cannot be destroyed by water or air or be attacked by bacteria. This explains why so many plastics do not disintegrate in the environment in the way that other materials do. Only sunlight can destroy some polymers, causing the chains to break and the material to become brittle.

combustion: the special case of oxidization of a substance in which a considerable amount of heat and usually light are given out. Combustion is often referred to as "burning."

compound: a chemical consisting of two or more elements chemically bonded together. Calcium atoms can combine with carbon atoms and oxygen atoms to make calcium carbonate, a compound of all three atoms.

plastic (material): a carbon-based material consisting of long chains (polymers) of simple molecules. The word plastic is commonly restricted to synthetic polymers.

plastic (property): a material is plastic if it can be made to change shape easily. Plastic materials will remain in the new shape. (Compare with elastic, a property whereby a material goes back to its original shape.)

▶ Butane gas is a hydrocarbon and contains carbon and hydrogen bonded together. When set alight, it burns, producing heat.

◀ Living organisms depend on carbon atoms for their existence. Tissues and bones or shells and wings are all carbon-based compounds.

◀ This is a piece of anthracite, a form of hard coal with a very high carbon content. Anthracite was formed by the slow decomposition of plant tissue under high temperature and pressure, deep within the Earth.

The Carboniferous Period is a part of geological time that began about 400 million years ago and lasted for some 60 millions years. In the 19th century geologists working in Britain recognized that much of the coal they were mining was formed during the same part of the Earth's history. Because coal is a carbon-based compound, they called the entire period the Carboniferous.

In fact, the Carboniferous Period contains carbon-based rocks of two kinds. During the early part, many thick beds of limestone were laid down. These Carboniferous limestones are made of calcium carbonate and so are carbon-based rocks. They also contain large amounts of oil and natural gas (petroleum).

During the later part of the Carboniferous Period, the main coal-bearing rocks on Earth were formed, together with more oil and natural gas (petroleum).

Geologists now know that coal and petroleum deposits have formed in a great many geological periods and are still forming today.

Crystals of carbon

Three minerals – graphite, diamond and the more recently discovered buckminsterfullerene (known as "buckyballs") – are made solely of carbon atoms. Of these, graphite is the most common. It occurs in rocks, and it is also formed as small crystals when hydrocarbons burn in the absence of air (e.g., coke, charcoal).

Diamond is far more rare than graphite. Diamonds were formed under immense temperatures and pressures, such as found in pipes leading to ancient volcanoes. The most famous diamond mine, at Kimberley, South Africa, follows an old volcanic pipe for more than two kilometers vertically into the Earth.

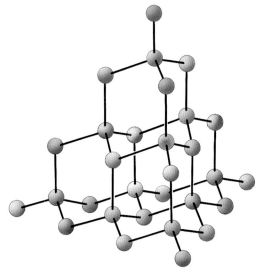

▲ This is the structure of diamond. It is built of interlocking carbon atoms with no room for other atoms to form part of the structure. This is what makes the mineral so unreactive.

Diamond: sparkling crystals of carbon

Carbon atoms can link to form a very stable mineral. Diamonds have atoms so tightly bonded together that they are one of the hardest substances known.

Pure diamond is colorless and transparent. It commonly forms a shape like two pyramids base to base (a tetrahedron). Jewelers make use of this property when they cut rough diamonds to make jewelry. Each of the faces (called facets) is created by splitting the diamond parallel to the faces of its crystals.

Diamond is not always colorless, and if it contains impurities, it may be a darker color. Some diamonds are almost black.

◀ This piece of Kimberlite rock shows the way that most diamond occurs, as a dull yellowish mineral set in a rock background. This diamond is translucent and highly flawed. Only occasionally does a transparent and flawless piece of mineral occur. The cut diamond placed on the rock shows the comparison.

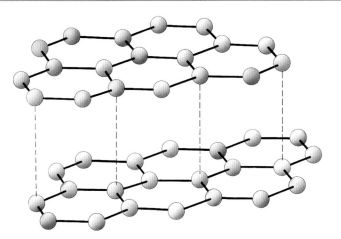

▲▶ This is the structure of graphite. It is made only of carbon minerals and is, like diamond, an unreactive substance. However, because the structure is in sheets, the bonds between the sheets are relatively weak, so that when pressure is applied, parts of the mineral flake off. This is what allows graphite to be used in pencils.

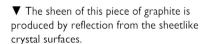

▼ The sheen of this piece of graphite is produced by reflection from the sheetlike crystal surfaces.

Graphite

Graphite is a black, soft form of carbon, harder than coal but far softer than diamond. Graphite naturally crumbles to release tiny flakes. This occurs because in graphite the carbon atoms are arranged in sheets that are poorly linked to each other. As a result, one sheet of crystals readily slides over another. It is this property that makes graphite useful as a lubricant (it is used to lubricate door locks, for example) and also as a pencil "lead" because it leaves a trail of black flakes as it is moved across paper.

Graphite can also conduct electricity and heat. Graphite makes the central electrode in dry batteries in many pieces of electrical equipment, such as the brushes in electric motors where sparks occur, as well as in huge steel furnaces.

The carbon cycle

The carbon cycle is the name given to the way that carbon is transferred between plants, animals, the atmosphere, rocks and oceans.

The carbon cycle is crucial to the way the planet works. It is a very complicated cycle, of which a simplified form is shown here.

The main reservoirs of carbon are in the air (in the form of carbon dioxide) and in rocks (either as limestone and chalk or as oil, natural gas and coal). The main transfers occur through the growth and death of plants (involving the chemical processes of photosynthesis, respiration and oxidation) and through the way people burn fossil fuels (involving the process of oxidation).

Animals

The proteins created by plants are used to make the tissues of animals, and they also provide sources of sugars, starches and fats. To release energy locked up as glucose, the sugars, starches and fats are combined with oxygen (they are oxidized). As sugars are oxidized, carbon dioxide and water are returned to the environment as part of the carbon cycle. As cells wear out or die, they are broken down into carbon dioxide, water and other simple compounds.

For the most part, plant and animal tissues are broken down by decomposing organisms and the elements returned to the environment for reuse. However, in some cases, tissues are not immediately broken down and recycled, but get buried and are preserved. This produces a store of energy in the form of fossil fuels. In this case the carbon cycle is interrupted until the fuels are burned or until erosion exposes them at the surface, at which point they oxidize.

Respiration

All animals produce carbon dioxide in their lungs. The lungs breathe in air containing oxygen and expel air containing carbon dioxide. This is called respiration.

Plants release carbon dioxide gas as they convert sugars for energy. This is also respiration.

> **EQUATION: Oxidation of glucose**
>
> *Glucose + oxygen ⇨ carbon dioxide + water*
>
> $C_6H_{12}O_6(s) + 6O_2(g) \Rightarrow 6CO_2(g) + 6H_2O(l)$

▼ This diagram represents the way that sugars are oxidized during respiration to produce carbon dioxide gas. During photosynthesis this reaction is reversed.

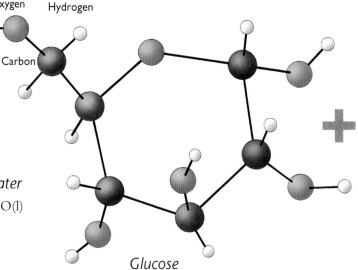

Oxygen Hydrogen

Carbon

Glucose

Plants

Only living plants can make compounds of carbon. They use the energy of sunlight in a process called photosynthesis.

In photosynthesis six molecules of carbon dioxide from the air combine with six molecules of water, forming one molecule of glucose (sugar) and releasing six molecules of oxygen back into the atmosphere.

Some sugar is combined with nitrogen compounds to form the proteins that make up tissues.

Sugar is also converted into larger, more complex molecules called starches and fats. These are forms of energy that can be stored for later use.

Plants release carbon dioxide when they are burned (a rapid form of decay).

▶ The natural carbon cycle. Note that, in addition, over geologic time carbon is stored in rocks. It is released when fossil fuels are burned.

fossil fuels: hydrocarbon compounds that have been formed from buried plant and animal remains. High pressures and temperatures lasting over millions of years are required. The fossil fuels are coal, oil and natural gas.

molecule: a group of two or more atoms held together by chemical bonds.

oxidation: a reaction in which the oxidizing agent removes electrons.

photosynthesis: the process by which plants use the energy of the Sun to make the compounds they need for life. In photosynthesis six molecules of carbon dioxide from the air combine with six molecules of water, forming one molecule of glucose (sugar) and releasing six molecules of oxygen back into the atmosphere.

Plants make sugars by photosynthesizing carbon dioxide from the air.

The main source of carbon dioxide is the air.

As sugars are oxidized by plants for energy, carbon dioxide is released back into the air.

As sugars are oxidized by animals for energy, carbon dioxide is released back to the air.

Carbon-based chemicals are absorbed by animals as they consume plant matter.

Organisms in the soil break down dead plant and animal tissue, and carbon dioxide gas is released as it decays.

EQUATION: Photosynthesis

Carbon dioxide + water ⇨ glucose + oxygen

$6CO_2(g) + 6H_2O(l) \Rightarrow C_6H_{12}O_6(s) + 6O_2(g)$

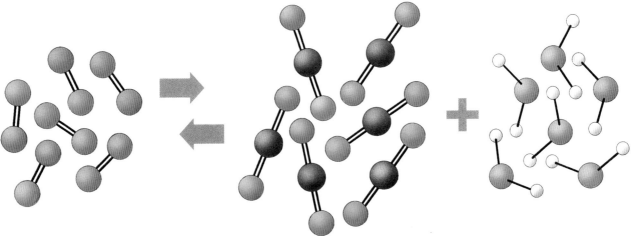

Oxygen   Carbon dioxide   Water

Carbon dioxide in the environment

Carbon dioxide gas (like water vapor) strongly absorbs, or soaks up, the heat that is radiated by the Earth out into space. Without carbon dioxide and water vapor, the Earth would be a very cold, almost uninhabitable place, some 25°C colder than it is today.

The amount of heat stored changes with the amount of carbon dioxide gas in the air. Over the last few centuries, people have increasingly burned more fuel, so much more carbon dioxide has been added to the air than was previously the case.

The extra carbon dioxide has been able to absorb even more of the earth's heat, leading to a gradual warming of the air. This process, known as the Greenhouse Effect, has been charted for more than a century.

Some scientists are concerned about the buildup of carbon dioxide because they fear that "global warming" will cause all sorts of unpredictable changes, such as droughts and floods, as well as a possibly disastrous rise in the sea level as the warm air causes the Antarctic ice sheet to melt.

▲ Plants need carbon to make the cells of their bodies. They extract carbon from carbon dioxide gas using the energy in sunlight.

Also...

The Earth absorbs energy through solar radiation. This is mostly short wave radiation. The gases in the atmosphere are largely transparent to solar radiation. The incoming solar radiation does little to warm the air, therefore, and mainly warms the land and oceans.

The wavelength of radiation depends on the temperature of the radiating body. The Sun is very hot and so radiates in short wavelengths. However, the Earth is cool and radiates in longer (infrared) wavelengths.

Water vapor and carbon dioxide gas both absorb in the infrared wavelengths better than in short wavelengths, so they absorb some of the heat energy that would otherwise be lost to space. This is what makes the atmosphere warmer and causes the Greenhouse Effect.

▶ The passage of long wave radiation from the earth and back to space is slowed by the increasing "blanket" of carbon dioxide in the atmosphere as more of the gas is released by burning fossil fuels.

▶ The decay of organic matter is important in releasing carbon to the cycle. Normally leaves decay within a few years, which is why there is rarely thick leaf litter on the ground. Only where the ground is permanently waterlogged, such as in still-water marshes and bogs, can organic material accumulate. When it does so, it locks up carbon. Major swamps have occurred in many periods of geological history. These eventually became buried, forming coal deposits, oil and natural gas reserves.

▼ Clear-cutting trees has a major effect on the natural carbon cycle because it removes part of a natural carbon-absorbing part of the environment (called a carbon "sink"). To maintain balance in the carbon cycle, trees have to be replanted in the same quantities that they are felled. This is happening in the temperate lands, but not in the tropics.

Using carbon dioxide

Carbon dioxide is sometimes used in its solid form – as dry ice – to create the impression of fog. It is safe, clean and easy to control in theaters because of three important properties: carbon dioxide sublimes, is heavier than air and is noncombustible.

Carbon dioxide gas is produced during the preparation of both food and drink, in some cases for effect (as in carbonated water), in other cases to "lighten" dough, cakes and pastries.

▲ Fizzy drinks contain carbonated water, that is, water in which carbon dioxide has been dissolved under pressure. In some cases the carbon dioxide is formed in the bottle or can by mixing an acid (such as phosphoric acid) and an alkali with the drink just before it is sealed in its container. These react to produce gas, although the gas remains dissolved while the container is closed.

When the cap is loosened, the pressure is reduced and the carbon dioxide comes out of solution, producing bubbles: the fizz.

Baking

The lightness of many baked flour-based foods depends on the dough, pastry, etc., containing a large number of bubbles of carbon dioxide gas. This can be achieved by heating baking soda (sodium bicarbonate), causing it to decompose, releasing carbon dioxide gas.

Baking powder is a mixture of baking soda (sodium bicarbonate), tartaric acid, and small amounts of starch. As soon as the acid and the baking soda are made wet they begin to react, releasing carbon dioxide. The amount and size of the bubbles depend on the rate at which the gas bubbles are created, larger bubbles being released by greater amounts of gas.

Carbon dioxide gas is usually used to lighten the texture of (or leaven) doughs, sweet pastries and cakes.

▶ This cake shows how carbon dioxide bubbles form from the reaction of baking powder. The bubbles become trapped by the stickiness of the dough, thus giving cakes their light texture.

Dry ice

Frozen carbon dioxide is called dry ice and is used for portable refrigeration and to create swirling fog on theater stages or movie sets.

EQUATION: Producing carbon dioxide by heating baking soda

Sodium bicarbonate ⇨ sodium carbonate + carbon dioxide + water

$$2NaHCO_3(s) \Rightarrow Na_2CO_3(s) + CO_2(g) + H_2O(l)$$

Preparation of carbon dioxide gas

Carbon dioxide gas can be produced in numerous ways in the laboratory. For example, if dilute hydrochloric acid is added to calcium carbonate, it begins to fizz. The reaction produces a solution of calcium chloride and releases carbon dioxide gas.

gelatinous: a term meaning made with water. Because a gelatinous precipitate is mostly water, it is of a similar density to water and will float or lie suspended in the liquid.

noncombustible: a substance that will not burn.

reagent: a starting material for a reaction.

sublimation: the change of a substance from solid to gas, or vice versa, without going through a liquid phase.

EQUATION: Preparation of carbon dioxide gas

Dilute hydrochloric acid + calcium carbonate ⇨ calcium chloride + carbon dioxide + water

$$2HCl(aq) \quad + \quad CaCO_3(s) \quad ⇨ \quad CaCl_2(aq) \quad + \quad CO_2(g) \quad + \quad H_2O(l)$$

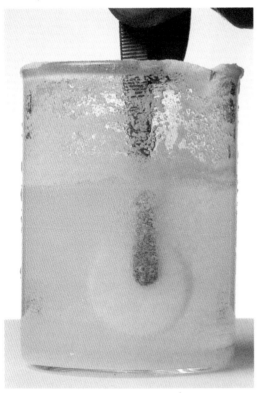

▼ Some antacid tablets contain calcium carbonate, which acts on the dilute hydrochloric acid in the stomach. This demonstration shows that a reaction occurs in the stomach, releasing carbon dioxide gas. This explains why some antacid tablets cause people to "burp."

Carbon dioxide as a fire extinguisher gas

Because carbon dioxide gas is noncombustible, it is ideal for use in extinguishing fires.

Fire extinguishers may contain two reagents (liquids that will react) to produce carbon dioxide quickly. The equation below shows the reaction of aluminum sulfate and sodium carbonate. These reagents were used as a source of carbon dioxide gas and a source of foam for many years until they were replaced by pressurized carbon dioxide cylinders.

In use, the two reagents are kept apart inside the extinguisher. When in use, a knob on the extinguisher is struck, breaking the seal between the liquids and causing them to react.

The reaction produces a gelatinous liquid and carbon dioxide gas. This gas cannot easily escape through this sticky liquid and instead forms bubbles inside it. The result is that a foam containing carbon dioxide immediately issues from the extinguisher nozzle. This has the effect of blanketing the fire with materials that will not burn. It also prevents oxygen from reaching the flames.

Also...

Many modern carbon dioxide extinguishers do not rely on a chemical reaction, but instead contain carbon dioxide gas under pressure in a strong cylinder.

EQUATION: Fire extinguishing

Aluminum sulfate (alum) + sodium carbonate + water ⇨ aluminum hydroxide (gelatinous precipitate) + carbon dioxide (gas) + sodium sulfate (solution)

$$Al_2(SO_4)_3(aq) \ + \ 3Na_2CO_3(aq) \ + \ 3H_2O(l) \ ⇨ \ 2Al(OH)_3(s) \ + \ 3CO_2(g) \ + \ 3Na_2SO_4(aq)$$

Carbon monoxide

Carbon monoxide is a reducing agent, that is, it takes oxygen from some materials it contacts. This is a useful reaction, and carbon monoxide is used widely in industry, especially in the refining of metals from their ores. For example, the chemical reactions inside a blast furnace involve the reduction of iron ore to iron metal.

However, carbon monoxide is also produced when fuels are burned because the burning is not usually efficient enough to produce only carbon dioxide. Unless exhaust gases from burning fuels are allowed to disperse, this colorless, tasteless and odorless gas can build up and be fatal.

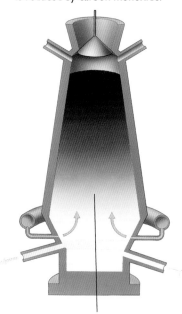

▼ A blast furnace in which iron oxide is reduced by carbon monoxide.

Carbon monoxide acts as a reducing agent in the heart of the furnace.

▼ A diagram of the way carbon monoxide is produced during fuel ignition.

The gas and air mixture is compressed by the piston and ignited by an electric spark from the spark plug. The reaction is explosive and forces the piston down, completing a stroke.

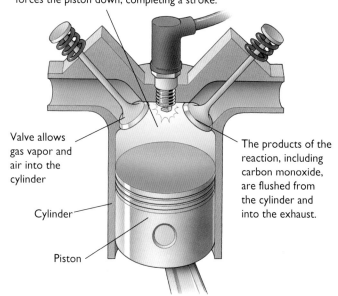

Valve allows gas vapor and air into the cylinder

The products of the reaction, including carbon monoxide, are flushed from the cylinder and into the exhaust.

Cylinder

Piston

Also...

Catalytic converters used in motor-vehicle exhausts are designed in part to cause the conversion of carbon monoxide to carbon dioxide and water. They achieve this by using the oxygen from another exhaust gas, nitric oxide. Single atoms of oxygen are very reactive and so readily combine with carbon monoxide to form carbon dioxide.

Inefficient combustion

In a typical internal combustion engine, the fuel is a hydrocarbon in the form of a mist of tiny droplets. When mixed with air and ignited with a hot object such as the spark plug in a car engine, the hydrocarbon reacts violently to produce hot gas.

If the engine were completely efficient, all the energy in the hydrocarbon would be turned into power to drive the cylinders. At the same time, the carbon would turn into harmless carbon dioxide. But no engine is very efficient, and the carbon does not burn up completely. As a result, carbon monoxide gas is also produced.

Carbon monoxide can be fatal because, when breathed into the lungs, the red blood cells absorb it instead of oxygen. As a result, oxygen cannot get to the brain. For this reason good ventilation is needed whenever engines are working inside a building.

Carbon monoxide in the atmosphere slowly changes to carbon dioxide as it combines with oxygen in the air.

EQUATION: Iron oxide reduced by carbon monoxide

Iron oxide + carbon monoxide ⇨ iron metal + carbon dioxide

$$Fe_2O_3(s) \quad + \quad 3CO(g) \quad ⇨ \quad 2Fe(l) \quad + \quad 3CO_2(g)$$

catalyst: a substance that speeds up a chemical reaction but itself remains unaltered at the end of the reaction.

oxidation/reduction: a reaction in which oxygen is gained/lost.

Carbon monoxide as a reducing agent

This laboratory demonstration shows how carbon monoxide can act as a reducing agent, taking oxygen from a metal ore. It is an example of a refining technique widely used in industry.

The glass tube contains black copper oxide. Carbon monoxide gas is blown through the tube, and the surplus is ignited and burns with a blue flame from a small hole in the tube.

Notice how the copper changes to an orange color. The heat of the Bunsen burner is speeding up the reaction of the carbon monoxide with the copper oxide, producing carbon dioxide gas and leaving pure copper behind.

The way that carbon monoxide takes up oxygen can also be used in industry to refine metal. A blast furnace, used to produce iron from iron ore, uses coke and air to produce the carbon monoxide and the heat needed to release the iron from its ore.

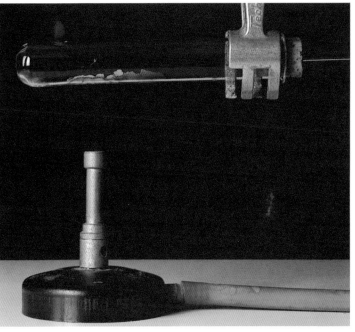

❶▲ Carbon monoxide is passed over the black copper oxide powder (copper ore) in a test tube. The glowing surface shows where the reaction between copper oxide and carbon monoxide is occurring. As the carbon monoxide exits the tube it is burned, producing a characteristic blue flame.

❷▼ The reduced copper oxide changes color as the oxygen is removed. The material left is pure copper.

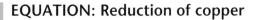

EQUATION: Reduction of copper

Copper oxide + carbon monoxide ⇨ carbon dioxide + copper

$$CuO(s) \quad + \quad CO(g) \quad \underset{\text{heat}}{⇨} \quad CO_2(g) \quad + \quad Cu(s)$$

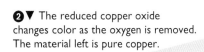

Carbon in food

Carbohydrate is the name for a wide range of natural compounds such as sugar and starch containing carbon, hydrogen and oxygen.

The simplest carbohydrate is glucose. This in turn is used to make proteins that build plant tissues called cellulose. Soft forms of cellulose make up the fleshy parts of leaves, for example, while a harder, reinforced form of cellulose called lignin makes up the veins of leaves, twigs, bark, etc.

Carbohydrates are a store of energy used both by plants and by animals when they eat plants. In this way the energy from the Sun is converted into energy for all living things.

Because they are so rich in energy, carbohydrates form the main part of most people's diets.

Fossilized carbohydrates (fossil plant tissues) are also the source of the fuels burned as coal and oil.

❶▲ Concentrated sulfuric acid is added to white sugar.

❷▶ It begins to froth and turn brown. This is an exothermic reaction, so a considerable amount of heat is given off in the water, producing steam.

◀ Typical carbohydrate-containing foods include potatoes, pasta and rice.

Oxidation of carbohydrates

The body makes use of carbohydrates by the process of oxidation. It is the reverse of photosynthesis. Plants store the carbohydrate glucose as starch and sucrose. In animals, glucose is sent around the body in the bloodstream, and any excess is converted to fat and stored for later use.

EQUATION: Oxidation of glucose

Glucose + oxygen ⇨ water + carbon dioxide (+ a release of energy)

$C_6H_{12}O_6(s) \quad + \quad 6O_2(g) \quad ⇨ \quad 6H_2O(l) \quad + \quad 6CO_2(g) \quad (+ \text{ energy released})$

Sulfuric acid dehydrates sugars

If sulfuric acid is added to sugar (sucrose), the sugar dehydrates, that is, it loses its water and turns into black carbon.

The reaction produces considerable heat, so water is released as steam. The chemical equation shows that the sulfuric acid remains uncombined.

As the steam is given off, bubbles form, which causes the carbon to develop into a "volcano" of a substance which, on cooling, has the feel of coke.

dehydration: the removal of water from a substance by heating it, placing it in a dry atmosphere or using a drying agent.

glucose: the most common of the natural sugars. It occurs as the polymer known as cellulose, the fiber in plants. Starch is also a form of glucose. The breakdown of glucose provides the energy that animals need for life.

oxidation: a reaction in which the oxidizing agent removes electrons. (Note that oxidizing agents do not have to contain oxygen.)

❹▼ The expanding bubbles are trapped in the carbon as the reaction finishes and the carbon cools to a cokelike hard material.

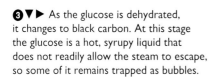

❸▼▶ As the glucose is dehydrated, it changes to black carbon. At this stage the glucose is a hot, syrupy liquid that does not readily allow the steam to escape, so some of it remains trapped as bubbles.

EQUATION: Dehydration of sucrose

Sucrose + sulfuric acid ⇨ water + carbon + sulfuric acid

$$C_{12}H_{22}O_{11}(s) + H_2SO_4(aq) \Rightarrow 11H_2O(g) + 12C(s) + H_2SO_4(aq)$$

Separating carbon compounds

Organic materials, those containing carbon, are mainly very chemically complex; however, this is not always noticable. For example, the red juice from, say, a beetroot may not at first sight seem complex at all.

But just as there are ways of showing that the simple color of white light is in fact made of many colors of light combined, so it is possible to show that a "simple" juice is made of an extraordinary array of chemicals, each one containing different carbon compounds. On these pages you can see how this is done using the process of chromatography.

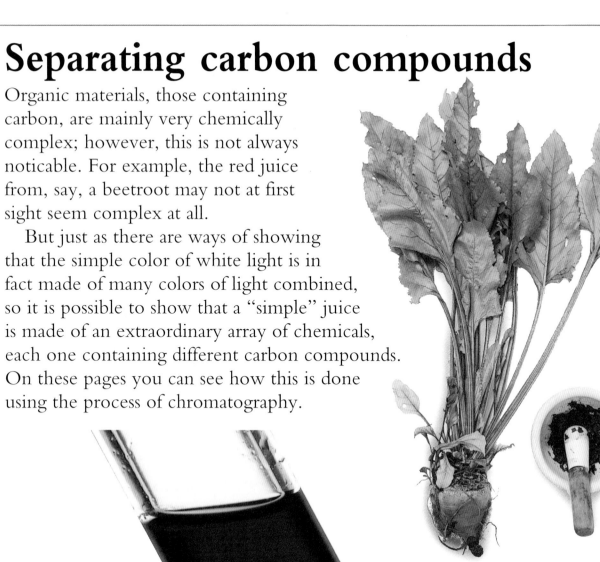

❶▲ The beetroot is first prepared by crushing it using a pestle and mortar.

Also...

The process demonstrated here is an example of chromatography, the use of a compound that does not react to separate out the components of a complex mixture (in this case a vegetable dye). A substance like aluminum oxide, used in this way, is called a stationary phase. Substances easily attach to its surface (a process called adsorption) and are also easily washed off again. Each substance "sticks" to the aluminum oxide to a different degree, so that the least firmly stuck can be washed off most easily, and so on. As a result, the various compounds making up the original substance wash out of the base of the column one at a time and can be collected separately.

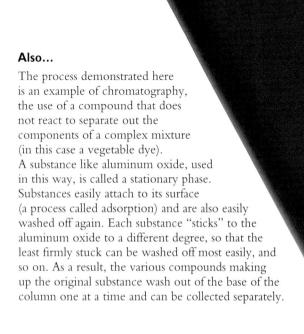

❷◀ The beetroot juice is diluted with a liquid in which it can dissolve (in this case acetone).

Crushed beetroot leaves

Acetone

3 ◀ A column of aluminum oxide is prepared by filling it with acetone. The aluminum oxide acts as a chemical filter, releasing the components of the juice one at a time.

Aluminum oxide

Cotton wool support

Rubber stopper with hole

acetone: a petroleum-based solvent.

mixture: a material that can be separated into two or more substances using physical means.

4 ◀ The first component of the beetroot juice emerges from the base of the tube. It is a yellow substance.

5 ▼ These are the first two components collected from the tube. Notice that they are slightly different colors. The substance on the right is chlorophyll (the green pigment in plants), while that on the left is called xanthophyll.

Separated components of the beetroot drip from the the column into a test-tube

Charcoal

Charcoal is wood that has been burned at about 1000°C in the absence of air. It is almost pure carbon and consists of tiny crystals of graphite.

Charcoal is able to burn at much higher temperatures than wood, and it is smokeless, so it makes a good fuel.

Activated charcoal is a form of charcoal made by burning waste organic matter (twigs, wood bark, sawdust, etc.) in the absence of air. When it has been processed, it has an enormous surface area that is able to absorb molecules of gas. For this reason it is often used when gas molecules need to be absorbed as in gas masks.

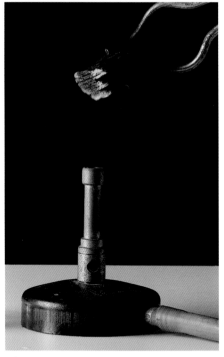

▲ Charcoal glows when it is heated with a gas jet from a Bunsen burner. Notice that the charcoal burns without any smoke; all of the graphite crystals are fused together in the charcoal and thus are not released as soot particles.

▼ Because it is made from wood, charcoal is an attractive fuel in the developing world where people need a fuel that provides a high temperature for cooking but where they cannot afford to use electricity, bottled gas or kerosene. Charcoal is also made into briquettes and used for barbecue fires in industrial countries.

Carbon black

When people are asked what color they associate with carbon, they usually say black. If people are asked to name a common form of carbon, they often say soot.

In fact black soot (called lampblack) from badly adjusted oil lamps, for example, is almost pure carbon. Pure carbon, a deep black powder such as is used in photocopiers and laser printers, is obtained by heating anything containing carbon – coal and wood, for example – in a furnace where there is no air. As a result, coal changes to coke and wood to charcoal.

Powdered carbon contains spheres of the rare form of carbon called buckminsterfullerene. Powdered carbon is used in rubber and plastics to slow down the rate at which these materials deteriorate in sunlight. Carbon powder is also used to make black ink and paint.

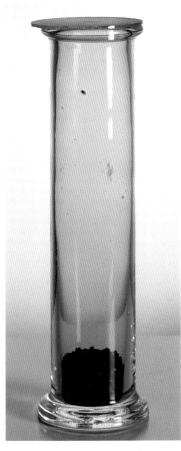

❶◄ A piece of activated charcoal has been dropped into a gas jar containing bromine and the cover glass replaced.

❷▼ Within a minute the color of the gas is getting lighter as fewer free bromine molecules remain in the jar.

adsorb: to "collect" gas molecules or other particles onto the *surface* of a substance. They are not chemically combined and can be removed. (The process is called "adsorption.")

halogen: one of a group of elements including chlorine, bromine, iodine and fluorine.

❸▼ After a few minutes the gas jar is colorless because all of the bromine molecules are now adsorbed onto the surface of the activated charcoal with none remaining as free gas.

Activated charcoal

Activated charcoal has a very large reactive surface area (about 2000 sq m of surface area for every gram in weight of charcoal). It is able to soak up (adsorb) large numbers of gas molecules on this vast surface.

This impressive property means that activated charcoal has been widely used as a gas filter, from gas masks for use in war or in fire-fighting, to removing unpleasant odors. It is also used in water-purification plants.

This sequence of pictures shows a gas jar, with activated charcoal in the bottom that has been filled with bromine, a poisonous, brown halogen gas. The pictures were taken over a few minutes. Notice how the amount of free bromine in the gas jar (as seen by the color of the gas) decreases. In the gas jar on the right there is no free bromine left at all.

Once all the sites on the activated charcoal have been used, the charcoal has to be thrown away. It cannot be reactivated. Although activated charcoal works well for many hydrocarbons, chlorine and similar gases, carbon will not absorb oxygen or nitrogen. Gas-suits with activated charcoal linings were used by the allied forces in the Gulf War because there was a threat of gas attack.

Hydrocarbons

The word petroleum comes from the Latin words *petra* and *oleum*, meaning "rock" and "oil," respectively. Petroleum is a "catchall" name for a range of hydrocarbon gases, liquids and some solids that form in the rocks of the Earth's crust.

Petroleum is usually a complicated mixture of liquids, solids and dissolved gases. The liquid form of petroleum is referred to as crude oil. The gases associated with petroleum are called natural gas. From these liquids and gases come the fuels that power the modern world and the raw materials for plastics, fertilizers, drugs and a wide range of other essential materials.

▲ Natural gas is predominantly made of the hydrocarbon methane, CH_4

▼ Crude oil is a brown, often sulfurous-smelling liquid. This sample is from the second well ever drilled in Texas.

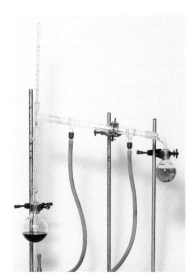

▲ The laboratory apparatus shown in the diagram on the right looks like this.

Also...

The most common carbon-based compounds contain simply hydrogen and carbon derived from living tissue. These are called hydrocarbons and they are the basis of most fuels such as coal, oil and gas.

Other groups of carbon-based compounds include alcohols such as ethanol, the substance found in all alcoholic beverages; acetone, which can dissolve many plastics; and esters, which smell like fruit.

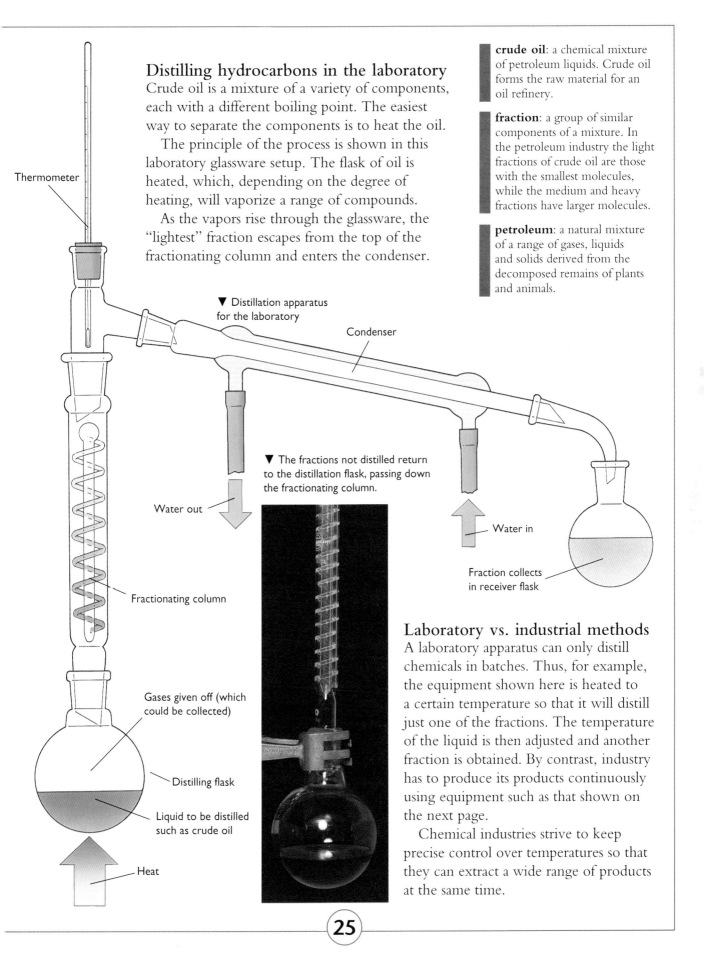

Distilling hydrocarbons in the laboratory

Crude oil is a mixture of a variety of components, each with a different boiling point. The easiest way to separate the components is to heat the oil.

The principle of the process is shown in this laboratory glassware setup. The flask of oil is heated, which, depending on the degree of heating, will vaporize a range of compounds.

As the vapors rise through the glassware, the "lightest" fraction escapes from the top of the fractionating column and enters the condenser.

crude oil: a chemical mixture of petroleum liquids. Crude oil forms the raw material for an oil refinery.

fraction: a group of similar components of a mixture. In the petroleum industry the light fractions of crude oil are those with the smallest molecules, while the medium and heavy fractions have larger molecules.

petroleum: a natural mixture of a range of gases, liquids and solids derived from the decomposed remains of plants and animals.

Thermometer

▼ Distillation apparatus for the laboratory

Condenser

Water out

▼ The fractions not distilled return to the distillation flask, passing down the fractionating column.

Water in

Fraction collects in receiver flask

Fractionating column

Gases given off (which could be collected)

Distilling flask

Liquid to be distilled such as crude oil

Heat

Laboratory vs. industrial methods

A laboratory apparatus can only distill chemicals in batches. Thus, for example, the equipment shown here is heated to a certain temperature so that it will distill just one of the fractions. The temperature of the liquid is then adjusted and another fraction is obtained. By contrast, industry has to produce its products continuously using equipment such as that shown on the next page.

Chemical industries strive to keep precise control over temperatures so that they can extract a wide range of products at the same time.

Processing crude oil

Processing crude oil to obtain petrochemicals provides us with some of the most valuable products in use today. This is carbon-chemistry in action. Processing is vital because petroleum is a complicated mixture of chemicals that cannot be used directly. The chemical sorting process is called refining.

In general the most usable fractions are light liquids, such as gasoline, and gases, such as butane. The least desirable are thick liquids. Thus a petrochemical plant has a second task: to break up, or "crack," the large molecules of the heavy thick liquid products to make more of those with higher demand.

Cracking is possible because hydrocarbons can be converted into one another quite easily. Cracking also has another benefit: if a petrochemical plant did not perform this valuable piece of chemistry, then the amount of waste liquid to be disposed of would be colossal.

Eventually the raw materials for a vast array of complicated products such as plastics, solvents, synthetic fibers, synthetic rubber as well as fuels and solvents can be produced.

▼ This is a fractionating tower from a refinery and is designed to distill a range of fractions. The fractions with the lowest boiling points condense at the top, whereas those with higher boiling points distill lower down.

At each level small bell caps allow vapors to rise and at the same time trap condensate so that it can be withdrawn from the column.

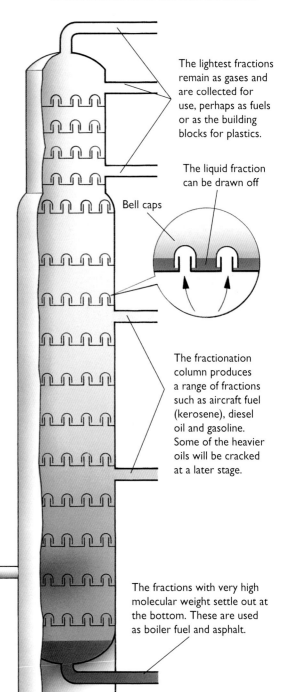

The lightest fractions remain as gases and are collected for use, perhaps as fuels or as the building blocks for plastics.

The liquid fraction can be drawn off

Bell caps

The fractionation column produces a range of fractions such as aircraft fuel (kerosene), diesel oil and gasoline. Some of the heavier oils will be cracked at a later stage.

Heated crude oil enters some way from the bottom.

The fractions with very high molecular weight settle out at the bottom. These are used as boiler fuel and asphalt.

◄ The tall, slim, towers are the fractionating towers of a petrochemical plant. The squat tower on the left is the cooling tower of a power station.

What a petrochemical plant does

A refinery is a collection of tall towers, called distillation towers, connected by a maze of pipes. The crude oil is heated in the towers so that the lighter parts of the mixture boil off, or vaporize. The compounds can be separated because petroleum is a mixture. This means that the separate fractions can be obtained by making use of the various boiling points of the substances in the mixture.

The gases then condense in the upper, cooler parts of the towers and form into liquids. By using a series of towers, the various chemicals can be separated. The aim is to produce such different products as liquified petroleum gas (LPG), gasoline (vehicle fuel), kerosene (aircraft fuel), heating oil, diesel fuel and asphalt (for road surfaces).

A simple process of boiling only separates about a tenth of the crude oil. The remainder has to be processed again, using a procedure called "cracking," which involves splitting the large, heavy hydrocarbon molecules into smaller ones. A variety of methods is used, including heat and pressure, vacuum and chemicals such as hydrogen. In this way the products of the refinery can be tailored to market needs. So, for example, if the demand is for an increase in lubricating oils, then the cracking process is adjusted to produce these products; if the oil demand falls and the gasoline demand rises, the type of cracking is changed to give the new balance of products.

cracking: breaking down complex molecules into simpler components. It is a term particularly used in oil refining.

crude oil: a chemical mixture of petroleum liquids. Crude oil forms the raw material for an oil refinery.

fraction: a group of similar components of a mixture. In the petroleum industry the light fractions of crude oil are those with the smallest molecules, while the medium and heavy fractions have larger molecules.

petroleum: a natural mixture of a range of gases, liquids and solids derived from the decomposed remains of plants and animals.

▼ A diagrammatic representation of the cracking process.

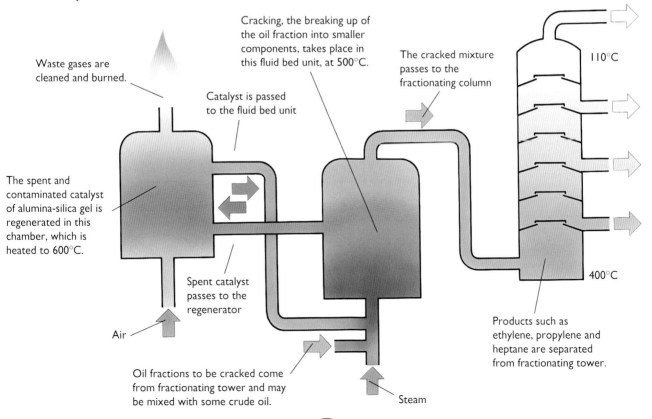

Waste gases are cleaned and burned.

Cracking, the breaking up of the oil fraction into smaller components, takes place in this fluid bed unit, at 500°C.

Catalyst is passed to the fluid bed unit

The cracked mixture passes to the fractionating column

110°C

The spent and contaminated catalyst of alumina-silica gel is regenerated in this chamber, which is heated to 600°C.

Spent catalyst passes to the regenerator

Air

Oil fractions to be cracked come from fractionating tower and may be mixed with some crude oil.

Steam

400°C

Products such as ethylene, propylene and heptane are separated from fractionating tower.

Variety in organic compounds

Carbon chemistry relies heavily on the use of hydrocarbon products obtained from petroleum. On these two pages you can see the structure of some common hydrocarbon substances.

Alkanes (paraffins)

Carbon atoms always form four chemical bonds, that is, they can each bond to four other atoms. All hydrocarbons in which the carbon atoms are joined by a "single" bond have a name that ends in –ane, such as ethane, methane and butane.

▲ Butane gas is used in cooking stoves.

▼ This represents a molecule of ethane. Ethane, butane and pentane gases are obtained from the top of a fractionating column (see page 26).

▼ This represents a molecule of butane.

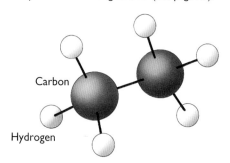

Carbon

Hydrogen

Carbonyl compounds and alcohols

Carbon atoms can use two bonds to join to an oxygen atom, as in the case of the solvent acetone, as well as bonding to oxygen by a single bond, as in the alcohol called ethanol.

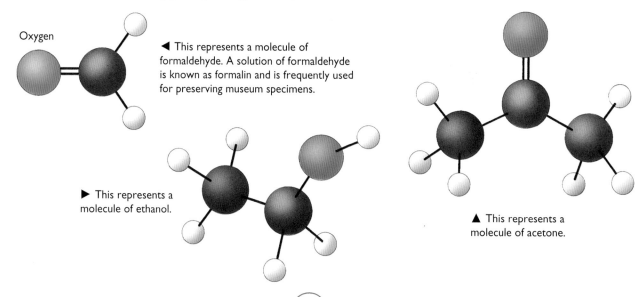

Oxygen

◀ This represents a molecule of formaldehyde. A solution of formaldehyde is known as formalin and is frequently used for preserving museum specimens.

▶ This represents a molecule of ethanol.

▲ This represents a molecule of acetone.

Unsaturated hydrocarbons

Carbon atoms may be joined together with a double bond as in ethylene or by a triple bond such as acetylene (whose modern name is ethyne). Acetylene can be used in cutting and welding flames; it requires an oxygen supply if it is to combust completely to form carbon dioxide and water.

polymerization: a chemical reaction in which large numbers of similar molecules arrange themselves into large molecules, usually long chains. This process usually happens when there is a suitable catalyst present. For example, ethylene reacts to form polyethylene in the presence of certain catalysts.

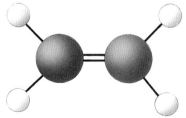

▲ This represents a molecule of ethylene.

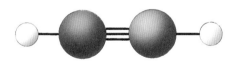

▲ This represents a molecule of ethyne.

Solvents, fats and flavors (esters)

Other groups of atoms found in organic compounds include the "ester" groups, for example, ethyl ethanoate (also known as ethyl acetate), which makes nail-polish remover.

Simple esters are flavoring essences and solvents. Those with a greater number of carbon and hydrogen atoms are cooking oils and fats.

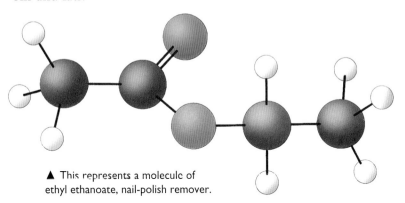

▲ This represents a molecule of ethyl ethanoate, nail-polish remover.

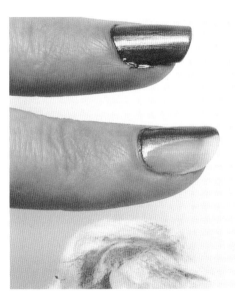

▲ Nail polish can be removed using a solvent, nail-polish remover, made from ethyl acetate.

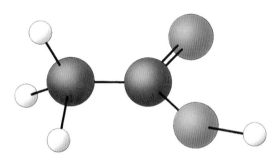

▲ Two oxygen atoms are also present in organic acids such as acetic acid (best known as vinegar).

Also...
Hydrocarbons: the foundation of organic chemistry

The major branch of chemistry that deals with hydrocarbons is often called organic chemistry. This is a historical name, from the mistaken belief that such compounds could only be made by living organisms. Today most of the compounds are made from petroleum in the laboratory or in a petrochemical plant.

The properties of plastics

Plastics are a group of carbon-based materials that scientists often refer to as polymers. They vary greatly, but they have a number of properties in common.

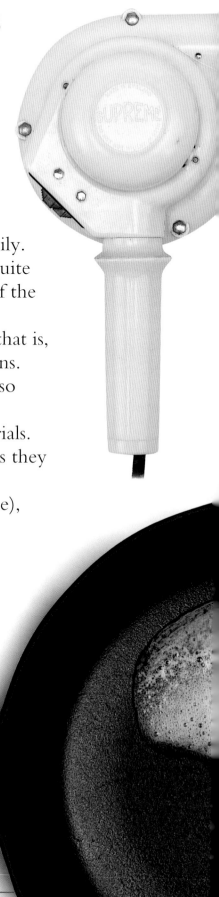

- Most plastics are not very strong and could not, for example, replace steel in uses such as the frames of buildings.
- Most plastics are easy to bend.
- Many plastics will change shape if they are pulled.
- Many plastics are not very hard and will scratch easily.
- Many plastics are not very dense, that is, they are quite lightweight materials. Some will float in water; most of the others are only just a little denser than water.
- Many plastics are very brittle at low temperatures, that is, they will harden and crack easily in very cold conditions.
- Many plastics soften easily when they get hot (and so cannot be used for things like oven-based cookware). However, there are exceptions, such as nonstick materials.
- Plastics expand about ten times as much as metals as they get hotter.
- Many plastics are destroyed by fire (they decompose), even though they do not actually burn.
- Most plastics are very good electrical insulators and so can be used to insulate cables, for plugs and sockets, etc.
- Plastics tend to become brittle with age. This is especially so with those exposed to direct sunlight (ultraviolet radiation).
- Plastics are mostly very resistant to being broken down by chemical attack, and they are not water-soluble, which is why they do not decompose when placed out in the open or buried.

Bakelite

Bakelite is a plastic that is based on the substances phenol and formaldehyde. It is a thermosetting plastic, meaning that when heat is applied, it hardens. Bakelite will not catch fire, and so was used instead of the inflammable celluloid.

◀ Bakelite appliance from the 1950s.

The history of plastics

The very first plastic, invented over a century ago, was called celluloid. It was a brittle white substance that was used as synthetic ivory. It was also used as the backing for rolls of photographic film.

It took half a century before the next plastic was invented. It was called Bakelite, after its inventor Leo Baekland. But then new forms of plastic were invented at a faster and faster rate.

The most well-known plastics are nylon and polyester (both widely used for making garments), and polyethylene and polystyrene (used for making containers and packaging materials).

Most recently there has been a trend to make custom plastics designed for a specific use.

plastic (material): a carbon-based material consisting of long chains (polymers) of simple molecules. The word plastic is commonly restricted to synthetic polymers.

plastic (property): a material is plastic if it can be made to change shape easily. Plastic materials will remain in the new shape. (Compare with elastic, a property whereby a material goes back to its original shape.)

polymer: a compound that is made of long chains by combining molecules (called monomers) as repeating units. ("Poly" means many, "mer" means part.)

Celluloid: the first plastic

Alexander Parkes made the first plastic in 1856. It was made from cellulose nitrate and camphor. Many nitrate compounds are used in explosives, and celluloid material was used in World War I as a smokeless explosive. Not surprisingly, one of the problems with celluloid in the home or office is that it catches fire very easily. As a result it is rarely used today.

On the other hand, cellulose, which is also prone to catch fire, is still widely used as a solvent for inks and paints because it dries very quickly. Car body paints, for example, are formulated with cellulose.

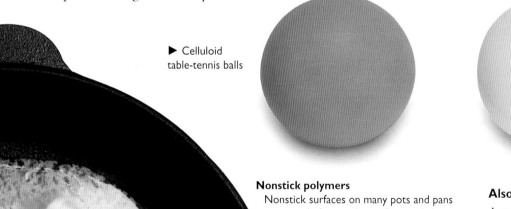

▶ Celluloid table-tennis balls

Nonstick polymers

Nonstick surfaces on many pots and pans are made from polytetrafluoroethylene (Teflon), which is based on the two simple chemicals fluorine and ethylene. It was invented in 1938. It does not dissolve or burn. This is why it can be used on pans and why fats, oils and other materials used in cooking have no effect on it.

◀ A modern nonstick frying pan with a Teflon surface.

Also... Plastics solvents

A solvent is a liquid chemical compound used for dissolving another compound without reacting with it. Most organic materials do not dissolve in water, so water cannot be used as a solvent.

Most solvents have a low boiling point and are volatile, that is, they evaporate easily. A solvent used in polymer-based paints is cellulose nitrate; a solvent for nail-polish (cellulose acetate) is ethyl acetate (see page 29).

Making polymers

Polymers are made in two ways: by adding building blocks together in long chains to produce materials known as addition polymers, and by removing water molecules to produce materials known as condensation polymers. These two types of polymer are important, and they produce such a wide range of everyday materials. On the next few pages is information on addition polymers; condensation polymers are described on page 36. The remainder of the book will look at some important polymers.

Addition polymerization

Some hydrocarbon molecules are very reactive and can be joined together, or polymerized. The reactive units are those in which carbon atoms are joined by a double bond. Ethylene, shown below, is an example.

To polymerize these units, or monomers, the double bond is broken and one bond used to join the unit to its neighbors. This builds long chains and is known as "addition polymerization."

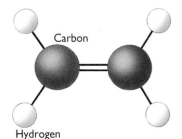
Carbon

Hydrogen

◀ This represents a molecule of ethylene. Units like this that can be polymerized are known as monomers.

▶ This represents a unit of addition polymerization derived from ethylene. The ethylene molecules join together to form the polymer polyethylene.

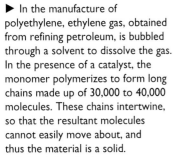

▶ In the manufacture of polyethylene, ethylene gas, obtained from refining petroleum, is bubbled through a solvent to dissolve the gas. In the presence of a catalyst, the monomer polymerizes to form long chains made up of 30,000 to 40,000 molecules. These chains intertwine, so that the resultant molecules cannot easily move about, and thus the material is a solid.

Polyethylene is cheap to manufacture and is used to make plastic bags and buckets. The properties of this polymer can be altered by substituting some or all of the hydrogens in the hydrocarbon chain with other elements or compounds. Some of these other polymers are shown on the opposite page.

A great range of polymers

Other monomers that produce addition polymers include tetrafluoroethylene, chloroethylene and styrene. These are shown below.

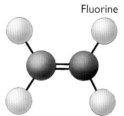
Fluorine

▶ In the case of tetrafluoroethylene all the hydrogen atoms on the ethylene molecule have been substituted by fluorine. The polymer is polytetrafluoroethylene (PTFE or Teflon), a hard plastic which is not attacked by most chemicals. It is used on such items as nonstick pans.

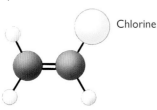
Chlorine

▶ In chloroethylene (vinyl chloride) a hydrogen atom has been substituted by chlorine. Its polymer is polychloroethylene (polyvinyl chloride or PVC).

▼ In styrene a hydrogen atom on the ethylene molecule has been replaced by a ring of carbon atoms, known as a benzene ring. Styrene is polymerized to produce polystyrene.

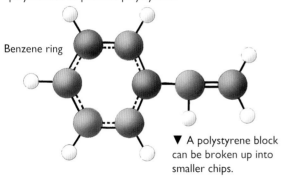
Benzene ring

▼ A polystyrene block can be broken up into smaller chips.

Polystyrene

Polystyrene (polyvinyl benzene), or Styrofoam as it is often called, is a hard, brittle plastic made by blowing air into the softened plastic. It is frequently used for insulation, and its light weight makes it ideal for packaging. However, it is very brittle and cannot withstand knocks as well as other plastics such as PVC.

Polystyrene is very hazardous in a fire because as it melts, molten globules flow away, carrying the fire with them and thus helping spread it.

catalyst: a substance that speeds up a chemical reaction but itself remains unaltered at the end of the reaction.

monomer: a building block of a larger chain molecule ("mono" means one, "mer" means part).

oxidize: the process of gaining oxygen. This can be part of a controlled chemical reaction, or it can be the result of exposing a substance to the air, where oxidation (a form of corrosion) will occur slowly, perhaps over months or years.

polymer: a compound that is made of long chains by combining molecules (called monomers) as repeating units. ("Poly" means many, "mer" means part.)

thermoplastic: a plastic that will soften and can repeatedly be molded it into shape on heating and will set into the molded shape as it cools.

Vinyl (PVC)

Vinyl, or PVC (polyvinyl chloride), is a form of plastic used widely as a furniture covering, in molded items such as washing bowls, electrical cable insulation, window frames, house panels and for many other items.

It is a thermosetting plastic, meaning that the objects have to be formed from the polymer while it is still a hot liquid. Once it has cooled and set it will retain the shape that it has been given and will not soften again.

Vinyl will harden and crack when exposed to ultraviolet light (a natural component of sunlight). It will also oxidize in air. To make it stable, give it attractive colors, and make it resistant to impacts, other materials have to be combined with it. Carbon powder, for example, is added to make the black-colored plastic that can be used for waste bags and other uses where the material will be exposed.

▲ This house siding and the window frames are made from u-PVC, which has been specially treated to prevent deterioration and discoloration when subject to ultraviolet light. This means that the house doesn't need to be painted, as similar, traditionally built houses would.

Rubber, a natural addition polymer

Rubber is the name of an elastic material that can be stretched to several times its own length before breaking. The word rubber originally referred to the material, known as latex, that is the sap of the rubber tree. However, a wide variety of synthetic rubbers is now also produced.

The rubber molccule is an example of a polymer, a giant molecule made of many (tens of thousands to millions) simple units arranged in a chain. The individual units (called monomers) are each about the size of a sugar molecule.

The rubber polymer is elastic because the long chains are linked together (called cross-linking). Each chain can be pulled slightly past each other chain. The cross-linking, however, pulls the chains back into their original place when the force is removed.

Rubbers can be made more strongly cross-linked using sulfur through a process called vulcanization. Vulcanization produces the very strong forms of rubber used for vehicle tires.

▲ ◀ Latex is tapped from rubber trees and then collected for processing. It is still a very labor-intensive operation.

▲▼ Rubber is used in a very wide range of products wherever elastic waterproof properties are required. In this factory rubber is being used to make gloves for laboratory use. The forms, made of a ceramic material, are dipped into a bath of latex, giving them a coating. The coated forms are transported through an oven, where the rubber dries. The gloves are pulled off the forms, and a drying powder is puffed into them to make them easier to pull on and off. Air is blown into each glove to test for defects. All the gloves used by the chemists in the demonstrations in this series of books were made on this Malaysian production line.

▶ Styrene, $C_6H_5CHCH_2$, is a hydrocarbon monomer. It is stored as a liquid, but on exposure to air it polymerizes, setting into the shape of the container. In much polymer chemistry, the polymer is formulated so that it has useful properties when solid.

latex: (the Latin word for "liquid"): a suspension of small polymer particles in water. The rubber that flows from a rubber tree is a natural latex. Some synthetic polymers are made as latexes, allowing polymerization to take place in water.

polymerization: a chemical reaction in which large numbers of similar molecules arrange themselves into large molecules, usually long chains. This process usually happens when there is a suitable catalyst present. For example, ethylene reacts to form polyethylene in the presence of certain catalysts.

vulcanization: forming cross-links between polymer chains to increase the strength of the whole polymer. Rubbers are vulcanized using sulfur when making tires and other strong materials.

Also... The history of rubber

Rubber was first noticed by Europeans when Christopher Columbus arrived in the Americas. Natural rubber is a suspension of about 30% rubber particles in water. It is a white latex sap that flows naturally from rubber trees if the bark is scored.

The first person to find a use for the material was Charles Macintosh, who, in 1823, discovered that it could be used to make fabric waterproof. However, because natural rubber has no cross-links, it is difficult to use, becoming sticky when hot and stiff when cold. In 1839 Charles Goodyear invented the technique of vulcanizing rubber by heating it with sulfur.

As early as 1826, Michael Faraday found that rubber was a polymer of the monomer isoprene. The first artificial rubber was made during World War II, when there was a shortage of natural rubber. Styrene and butadiene are now used as the foundation of the modern synthetic rubber industry because they are more easily obtained than isoprene. They are all derived from petroleum.

Condensation polymers

The alternative to addition polymerization is called condensation polymerization. In this process each stage in the polymer chain forms as a water molecule is expelled.

Many common fibers are formed by condensation polymerization, including nylon and polyester. Their structures are shown here and the way they are made is shown on the following pages.

Nylon

Organic compounds containing nitrogen are important substances. 1,6-diaminohexane can be polymerized with hexandioic acid, and less commonly heptandioic acid, to form a nylon. This is an example of condensation polymerization, where a water molecule is eliminated as every link in the polymer chain is formed.

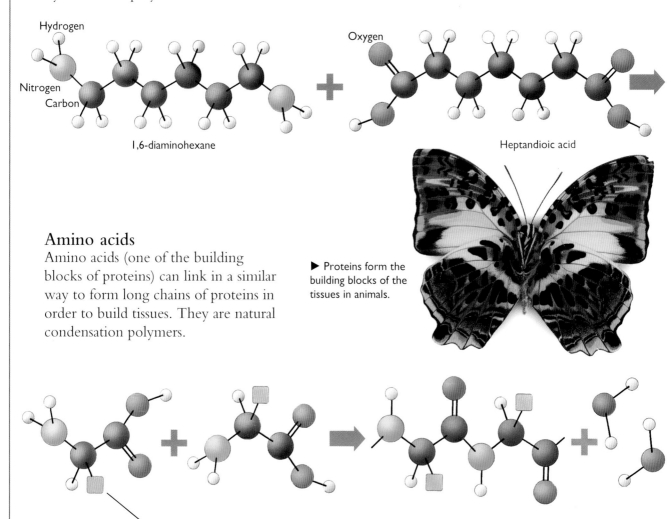

Hydrogen

Oxygen

Nitrogen

Carbon

1,6-diaminohexane

Heptandioic acid

Amino acids

Amino acids (one of the building blocks of proteins) can link in a similar way to form long chains of proteins in order to build tissues. They are natural condensation polymers.

▶ Proteins form the building blocks of the tissues in animals.

In the simplest amino acid, the shaded box would be a hydrogen atom. This section of the molecule is different for different amino acids.

A section of a protein chain

Water

◀ Synthetic fibers such as nylon and polyester are cheap to manufacture and are used for most modern clothing.

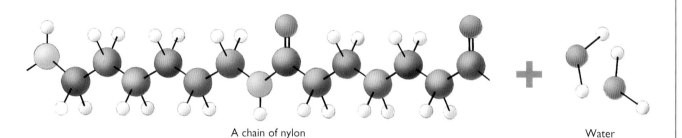

A chain of nylon   Water

Polyesters

The polyester Dacron is produced by heating a mixture of terephthalic acid and ethylene glycol.

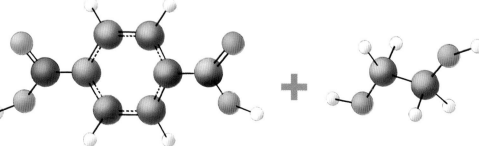

Terephthalic acid   Ethylene glycol

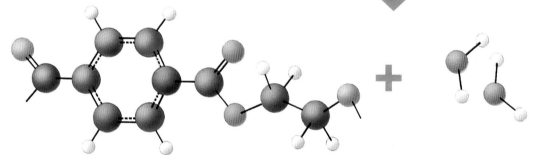

Section of a Dacron polymer chain   Water

Synthetic fibers

In the past, fibers were made from natural materials such as flax, wool and cotton; however, synthetic fibers are made from chemicals. The advantage of synthetic fibers over natural fibers is that the chemist can control the nature of the material closely to suit a specific purpose. On the other hand, natural fibers are so sophisticated that they will often perform functions that chemists do not yet know how to copy synthetically. Even so, synthetic fibers are very attractive because of their flexibility and strength. Many are stronger than metals.

The first fiber was rayon, a treated form of natural plant cellulose. The first entirely synthetic fiber was made in 1938. It was called nylon because it was due to collaboration between teams in New York (NY) and London (Lon). Like all fiber polymers, nylon is made into a syruplike substance and then extruded through tiny holes. The filaments (fibers) are then pulled out and wound onto a drum.

Synthetic fibers can be woven into cloth as mixtures to add durability to the material. Many coats, for example, are a mixture of polyester (which is hard wearing) and wool (which is warm and pleasant to the touch).

Synthetic fibers can also be incorporated into resins and made into composite materials with great strength.

Making nylon in the laboratory

A wide variety of plastics can be produced with simple techniques in the laboratory. The two chemicals used here are the organic chemicals 1,6-diaminohexane and hexan-dioyl chloride.

As one liquid is poured into the other, the chemical reaction immediately produces a white solid. This is nylon.

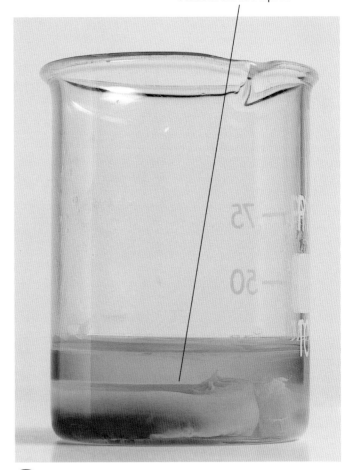

❶▼ 1,6-diaminohexane is poured carefully on to hexan-dioyl chloride. Here you can see the nylon forming at the interface between the two liquids.

②▼ The technique of spinning the nylon is used to produce a thread. To do this a piece of the nylon is picked out of the solution using tongs and is carefully lifted clear. Here you can see the difficulty of obtaining a filament with an even diameter. To achieve this the material needs to be lifted from the beaker at a constant rate.

polymer: a compound that is made of long chains by combining molecules (called monomers) as repeating units. ("Poly" means many, "mer" means part.)

solvent: the main substance in a solution (e.g., water in saltwater).

③▼ The filament begins to form. Here you can see that the filament can only be produced as long as the two liquids remain. As soon as the batch is used up, the process of picking a filament has to be repeated. Clearly, while the laboratory process shows that it is possible to produce filaments easily, industrial processes have to be found that make a more reliable filament in a continuous process. To do this the threads are extruded, not drawn, as shown on the next page.

Polyester fiber and film

Polyester is a carbon-chain material that is widely used as a synthetic fiber, and it can also be stretched out to make a film. It is not a natural filament, for example, cotton or wool. Instead, it is pushed out, or extruded, from a liquid through fine holes in a machine (called a spinneret) and then pulled into long filaments.

Polyester is a synthetic fabric made from woven filaments. It has been designed to be strong (it will not break easily when being woven on a machine), to stand up to many machine washes and to be easy to dye so that it can be made into many colors. It will also stretch and so be more comfortable for the wearer. The filaments can then be blended with natural fibers (to give more wear resistance than natural materials) or used on their own.

Some special forms of polyester fibers are given a hollow cross-section. This gives them the property of being good at insulating yet lightweight, so they can be used for warm clothing. Another form of polyester is made of microfibers, which make a mesh that keeps wind and water out yet allows body moisture to seep through.

▲▼ To make fibers, liquid polymer is extruded. The polymer typically arrives in the form of pellets, which are then heated to make a liquid. The liquid is then extruded through fine nozzles in the spinneret so that filaments (single strands) of plastic emerge. These are cooled and rapidly solidify so they can be twisted together to make a fiber.

▶ Hollow and microfiber polyester is widely used in clothing. In the case of sportswear the materials have to be waterproof and yet allow body moisture out. They have to resist the scuffing that comes from a fall, and they have to be lightweight so they do not unduly restrict movement.

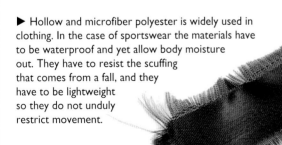

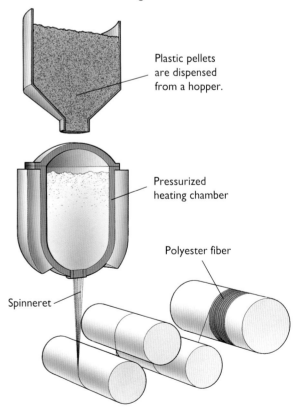

Plastic pellets are dispensed from a hopper.

Pressurized heating chamber

Polyester fiber

Spinneret

extrusion: forming a shape by pushing it through a die. For example, toothpaste is extruded through the cap (die) of the toothpaste tube.

synthetic: does not occur naturally but has to be manufactured.

▼ Filaments of polyester fiber are wound onto drums in a modern synthetic fiber factory

Also... Esters

The word "ester" refers to a group of organic compounds that includes many flavorings and also common solvents and plastics such as acetate (used as a backing on photographic film, for example). Esters are often made by reacting acids with alcohols.

Polyesters are polymers made with ester groups. Polymers used for coatings are made so that the polymers are cross-linked (as are rubbers). The form of polyester used for fibers is called polyethylene-terephthalate.

Polyesters can also be stretched into films such as the base of photographic films (when they are usually referred to simply as "acetate"). The sails on boats are also usually made from polyesters because of their strength and resistance to rotting.

▲ This photographic film is made from an ester normally called acetate.

Carbon-based chemicals and the environment

Carbon is found in nine-tenths of all the known compounds. In gases, it has also been used in making more synthetic materials than any other element. People are more concerned about the effects of synthetic materials because it is not always known how they react with people, animals and plants.

People are less concerned about the use of inorganic carbon-based compounds, such as limestone, than they are about organic carbon products, such as oil and coal. For example, the extraction of limestone from a quarry produces a limited environmental impact that can be understood and evaluated easily. The extraction of organic carbon-based chemicals produces much more complex problems. For example, some are made from forest products, and this can have grave implications for forest renewal. Many products are burned, adding to the Greenhouse Effect (see page 12). Oil is extracted from the ground and transported as a liquid, with the accompanying danger of possible oil spills.

Organic products cause concern because of the way they may interact with people and other living things. Many are designed as weedkillers, pesticides and so on, so it is possible that others produced for different purposes could have harmful side effects on living things. All this causes continuing concern, which is why regulation of the organic chemicals industry is so vital.

▲ Burning fossil fuels produces carbon dioxide in the air, adding to the Greenhouse Effect.

Pesticides and herbicides
Some carbon-based dyes and pesticides have been found to be very hazardous to health. The pesticide DDT, for example, was found to be very effective and was used all over the world. Years later, however, it was found to be very harmful to fish and birds, and its use is now banned in most parts of the world.

Oil
The main area of concern involves oil spills because the thick layers of oil take time to be oxidized to carbon dioxide gas or to be digested by organisms in water. Before natural processes can react with the oil, many animals are likely to die from ingesting the oil.

▶ Clearing up after the *Exxon Valdez* spill in Prince William Sound, Alaska.

Plastics

Another area of concern is in the use of plastics because these materials are inert, that is, they do not oxidize, are insoluble in water and cannot be digested by the organisms that normally cause decay.

Special formulations, used as substitutes for petroleum-based plastics and based on starches from plants, may help solve some of these problems for plastics used in packaging. These polymers decompose naturally in the wet conditions of the soil and so will decay in landfill sites.

▲ A polystyrene cup that will not decay

▶ Trash collection bags are now being designed to be disposable, as is some packaging.

oxidize: the process of gaining oxygen. This can be part of a controlled chemical reaction, or it can be the result of exposing a substance to the air, where oxidation (a form of corrosion) will occur slowly, perhaps over months or years.

Organic chemical releases

Sometimes fumes emanating from chemical plants can have disastrous effects, as they did in the Bhopal, India, incident in 1984. There a pesticide plant accidentally allowed water into a tank of methyl isocyanate. The result was the release of a toxic gas that killed 2,500 people and injured hundreds of thousands more.

The Periodic Table

Actinium (Ac)	89	Calcium (Ca)	20	Fermium (Fm)	100
Aluminum (Al)	13	Californium (Cf)	98	Fluorine (F)	9
Antimony (Sb)	51	Carbon (C)	6	Francium (Fr)	87
Americium (Am)	95	Cerium (Ce)	58	Gadolinium (Gd)	64
Argon (Ar)	18	Cesium (Cs)	55	Gallium (Ga)	31
Arsenic (As)	33	Chlorine (Cl)	17	Germanium (Ge)	32
Astatine (At)	85	Chromium (Cr)	24	Gold (Au)	79
Barium (Ba)	56	Cobalt (Co)	27	Hafnium (Hf)	72
Berkelium (Bk)	97	Copper (Cu)	29	Hassium (Hs)	108
Beryllium (Be)	4	Curium (Cm)	96	Helium (He)	2
Bismuth (Bi)	83	Dubnium (Db)	105	Holmium (Ho)	67
Bohrium (Bh)	107	Dysprosium (Dy)	66	Hydrogen (H)	1
Boron (B)	5	Einsteinium (Es)	99	Indium (In)	49
Bromine (Br)	35	Erbium (Er)	68	Iodine (I)	53
Cadmium (Cd)	48	Europium (Eu)	63	Iridium (Ir)	77

GROUPS ▶

PERIODS ▼

Transition metals

	1 (1)	2 (2)	(3)	(4)	(5)	(6)	(7)	(8)
1	1 **H** Hydrogen 1							
2	3 **Li** Lithium 7	4 **Be** Beryllium 9						
3	11 **Na** Sodium 23	12 **Mg** Magnesium 24						
4	19 **K** Potassium 39	20 **Ca** Calcium 40	21 **Sc** Scandium 45	22 **Ti** Titanium 48	23 **V** Vanadium 51	24 **Cr** Chromium 52	25 **Mn** Manganese 55	26 **Fe** Iron 56
5	37 **Rb** Rubidium 85	38 **Sr** Strontium 88	39 **Y** Yttrium 89	40 **Zr** Zirconium 91	41 **Nb** Niobium 93	42 **Mo** Molybdenum 96	43 **Tc** Technetium (99)	44 **Ru** Ruthenium 101
6	55 **Cs** Cesium 133	56 **Ba** Barium 137	71 **Lu** Lutetium 175	72 **Hf** Hafnium 178	73 **Ta** Tantalum 181	74 **W** Tungsten 184	75 **Re** Rhenium 186	76 **Os** Osmium 190
7	87 **Fr** Francium (223)	88 **Ra** Radium (226)	103 **Lr** Lawrencium (260)	104 **Rf** Rutherfordium (261)	105 **Db** Dubnium (262)	106 **Sg** Seaborgium (263)	107 **Bh** Bohrium (262)	108 **Hs** Hassium (265)

Legend

- Metals
- Metalloids (semimetals)
- Nonmetals
- Inner transition metals

Lanthanide series

57 **La** Lanthanum 139	58 **Ce** Cerium 140	59 **Pr** Praseodymium 141	60 **Nd** Neodymium 144

Actinide series

89 **Ac** Actinium (227)	90 **Th** Thorium (232)	91 **Pa** Protactinium (231)	92 **U** Uranium (238)

Iron (Fe)	26	Neptunium (Np)	93	Protactinium (Pa)	91	Strontium (Sr)	38	Ununoctium (Uuo)	118
Krypton (Kr)	36	Nickel (Ni)	28	Radium (Ra)	88	Sulfur (S)	16	Ununquadium (Uuq)	114
Lanthanum (La)	57	Niobium (Nb)	41	Radon (Rn)	86	Tantalum (Ta)	73	Unununium (Uuu)	111
Lawrencium (Lr)	103	Nitrogen (N)	7	Rhenium (Re)	75	Technetium (Tc)	43	Uranium (U)	92
Lead (Pb)	82	Nobelium (No)	102	Rhodium (Rh)	45	Tellurium (Te)	52	Vanadium (V)	23
Lithium (Li)	3	Osmium (Os)	76	Rubidium (Rb)	37	Terbium (Tb)	65	Xenon (Xe)	54
Lutetium (Lu)	71	Oxygen (O)	8	Ruthenium (Ru)	44	Thallium (Tl)	81	Ytterbium (Yb)	70
Magnesium (Mg)	12	Palladium (Pd)	46	Rutherfordium (Rf)	104	Thorium (Th)	90	Yttrium (Y)	39
Manganese (Mn)	25	Phosphorus (P)	15	Samarium (Sm)	62	Thulium (Tm)	69	Zinc (Zn)	30
Meitnerium (Mt)	109	Platinum (Pt)	78	Scandium (Sc)	21	Tin (Sn)	50	Zirconium (Zr)	40
Mendelevium (Md)	101	Plutonium (Pu)	94	Seaborgium (Sg)	106	Titanium (Ti)	22		
Mercury (Hg)	80	Polonium (Po)	84	Selenium (Se)	34	Tungsten (W)	74		
Molybdenum (Mo)	42	Potassium (K)	19	Silicon (Si)	14	Ununbium (Uub)	112		
Neodymium (Nd)	60	Praseodymium (Pr)	59	Silver (Ag)	47	Ununhexium (Uuh)	116		
Neon (Ne)	10	Promethium (Pm)	61	Sodium (Na)	11	Ununnilium (Uun)	110		

(9)	(10)	(11)	3 (12)	4 (13)	5 (14)	6 (15)	7 (16)	8 or 0 (17)	(18)
									2 **He** Helium 4
				5 **B** Boron 11	6 **C** Carbon 12	7 **N** Nitrogen 14	8 **O** Oxygen 16	9 **F** Fluorine 19	10 **Ne** Neon 20
				13 **Al** Aluminum 27	14 **Si** Silicon 28	15 **P** Phosphorus 31	16 **S** Sulfur 32	17 **Cl** Chlorine 35	18 **Ar** Argon 40
27 **Co** Cobalt 59	28 **Ni** Nickel 59	29 **Cu** Copper 64	30 **Zn** Zinc 65	31 **Ga** Gallium 70	32 **Ge** Germanium 73	33 **As** Arsenic 75	34 **Se** Selenium 79	35 **Br** Bromine 80	36 **Kr** Krypton 84
45 **Rh** Rhodium 103	46 **Pd** Palladium 106	47 **Ag** Silver 108	48 **Cd** Cadmium 112	49 **In** Indium 115	50 **Sn** Tin 119	51 **Sb** Antimony 122	52 **Te** Tellurium 128	53 **I** Iodine 127	54 **Xe** Xenon 131
77 **Ir** Iridium 192	78 **Pt** Platinum 195	79 **Au** Gold 197	80 **Hg** Mercury 201	81 **Tl** Thallium 204	82 **Pb** Lead 207	83 **Bi** Bismuth 209	84 **Po** Polonium (209)	85 **At** Astatine (210)	86 **Rn** Radon (222)
109 **Mt** Meitnerium (266)	110 **Uun** Ununnilium (272)	111 **Uuu** Unununium (272)	112 **Uub** Ununbium (277)		114 **Uuq** Ununquadium (289)		116 **Uuh** Ununhexium (289)		118 **Uuo** Ununoctium (293)

61 **Pm** Promethium (145)	62 **Sm** Samarium 150	63 **Eu** Europium 152	64 **Gd** Gadolinium 157	65 **Tb** Terbium 159	66 **Dy** Dysprosium 163	67 **Ho** Holmium 165	68 **Er** Erbium 167	69 **Tm** Thulium 169	70 **Yb** Ytterbium 173
93 **Np** Neptunium (237)	94 **Pu** Plutonium (244)	95 **Am** Americium (243)	96 **Cm** Curium (247)	97 **Bk** Berkelium (247)	98 **Cf** Californium (251)	99 **Es** Einsteinium (252)	100 **Fm** Fermium (257)	101 **Md** Mendelevium (258)	102 **No** Nobelium (259)

Understanding equations

As you read through Volumes 1 to 15 in the Elements set, you will notice that many pages contain equations using symbols. Symbols make it easy for chemists to write out the reactions that are occurring in a way that allows a better understanding of the processes involved. If you are not familiar with these symbols, these pages explain them.

Symbols for the elements

The basis for the modern use of symbols for elements dates back to the 19th century. At that time a shorthand was developed using the first letter of the element wherever possible.

Thus O stands for oxygen, H stands for hydrogen, and so on. However, if we were to use only the first letter, there could be some confusion. For example, nitrogen and nickel would both use the symbols N. To overcome this problem, many element symbols take the first two letters of the full name, with the second letter in lowercase. So, although nitrogen is N, nickel becomes Ni. Not all symbols come from the English name; many use the Latin name instead. That is why, for example, gold is not G but Au (from the Latin *aurum*), and sodium has the symbol Na (from the Latin *natrium*).

Compounds of elements are made by combining letters. So, the molecule carbon

Written and symbolic equations
In this book important chemical equations are briefly stated in words (they are called word equations) and are then shown in their symbolic form along with the states.

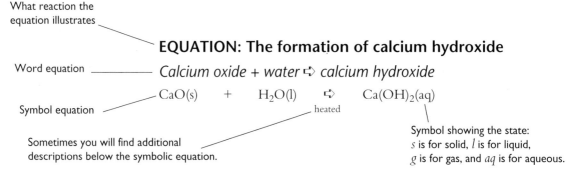

What reaction the equation illustrates

EQUATION: The formation of calcium hydroxide

Word equation —— *Calcium oxide + water ⇨ calcium hydroxide*

Symbol equation —— $CaO(s)$ + $H_2O(l)$ ⇨ $Ca(OH)_2(aq)$

heated

Sometimes you will find additional descriptions below the symbolic equation.

Symbol showing the state: s is for solid, l is for liquid, g is for gas, and aq is for aqueous.

Diagrams
Some of the equations are shown as graphic representations.

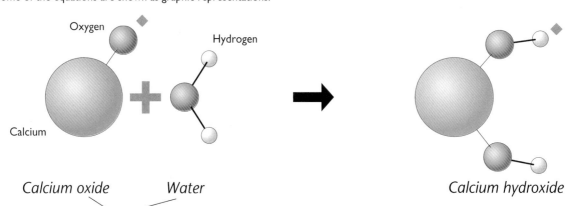

Oxygen

Hydrogen

Calcium

Calcium oxide   *Water*

Calcium hydroxide

Sometimes the written equation is broken up and put below the relevant stages in the graphic representation.

monoxide is CO. By using lowercase letters for the second letter of an element, it is possible to show that cobalt, symbol Co, is not the same as the molecule carbon monoxide, CO.

However, the letters can be made to do much more than this. In many molecules atoms combine in unequal numbers. So, for example, carbon dioxide has one atom of carbon for every two of oxygen. That is shown by using the number 2 beside the oxygen, and the symbol becomes CO_2.

In practice some groups of atoms combine as a unit with other substances. Thus, for example, calcium bicarbonate (one of the compounds used in some antacid pills) is written $Ca(HCO_3)_2$. This shows that the part of the substance inside the parentheses reacts as a unit, and the 2 outside the parentheses shows the presence of two such units.

Some substances attract water molecules to themselves. To show this, a dot is used. So, the blue form of copper sulfate is written $CuSO_4.5H_2O$. In this case five molecules of water attract to one of copper sulfate. When you see the dot, you know that this water can be driven off by heating; it is part of the crystal structure.

In a reaction substances change by rearranging the combinations of atoms. The way they change is shown by using the chemical symbols, placing those that will react (the starting materials, or reactants) on the left and the products of the reaction on the right. Between the two an arrow shows which way the reaction is going.

It is possible to describe a reaction in words. That produces word equations, which are given throughout Volumes 1 to 15. However, it is easier to understand what is happening by using an equation containing symbols. They are also given in many places. They are not shown when the equations are very complex.

In any equation both sides balance; that is, there must be an equal number of like atoms on both sides of the arrow. When you try to write down reactions, you, too, must balance your equation; you cannot have a few atoms left over at the end!

The symbols in parentheses are abbreviations for the physical state of each substance taking part, so that (*s*) is used for solid, (*l*) for liquid, (*g*) for gas, and (*aq*) for an aqueous solution, that is, a solution of a substance dissolved in water.

Atoms and ions

Each sphere represents a particle of an element. A particle can be an atom or an ion. Each atom or ion is associated with other atoms or ions through bonds – forces of attraction. The size of the particles and the nature of the bonds can be extremely important in determining the nature of the reaction or the properties of the compound.

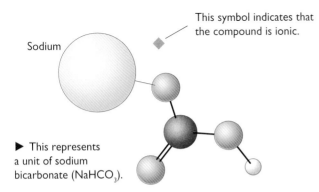

Sodium

This symbol indicates that the compound is ionic.

▶ This represents a unit of sodium bicarbonate ($NaHCO_3$).

The term "unit" is sometimes used to simplify the representation of a combination of ions.

Chemical symbols, equations, and diagrams

The arrangement of any molecule or compound can be shown in one of the two ways shown below, depending on which gives the clearer picture. The left-hand image is called a ball-and-stick diagram because it uses rods and spheres to show the structure of the material. This example shows water, H_2O. There are two hydrogen atoms and one oxygen atom.

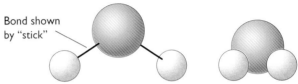

Bond shown by "stick"

Colors too

The colors of each of the particles help differentiate the elements involved. The diagram can then be matched to the written and symbolic equation given with the diagram. In the case above, oxygen is red, and hydrogen is gray.

Key facts about...

Name: carbon
Symbol: C
Atomic number: 6
Atomic weight: 12.01
Position in Periodic Table: group 4 (14)
(carbon group); period 2
State at room temperature: solid
Color: graphite is black, diamond is colorless
Density of solid: diamond: 3.52 g/cc;
graphite: 2.25 g/cc
Melting point: 3,550°C
Boiling point: 4,827°C
Origin of name: from the Latin word *carbo*,
meaning charcoal
Shell pattern of electrons: 2–4
*Further facts on this element can be found in
Volume 16: Actinium to Fluorine*

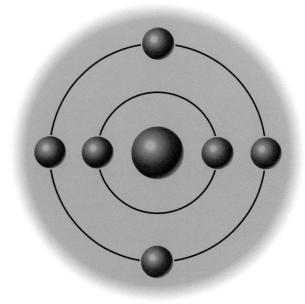

▲ The cutting down of trees has a major effect on the natural carbon cycle because it removes a natural carbon-absorbing part of the environment (called a carbon "sink"). To maintain balance in the carbon cycle, trees have to be replanted as they are felled. This is happening in the temperate lands, but not in the tropics.

▼ Coal is made of carbon and is an important fossil fuel.

Glossary of technical terms

absorb: to soak up a substance. Compare to adsorb.

adsorb: to "collect" gas molecules or other particles onto the *surface* of a substance. They are not chemically combined and can be removed. (The process is called "adsorption.")

acetone: a petroleum-based solvent.

amino acid: amino acids are organic compounds that are the building blocks for the proteins in the body.

catalyst: a substance that speeds up a chemical reaction but itself remains unaltered at the end of the reaction.

combustion: the special case of oxidization of a substance in which a considerable amount of heat and usually light are given out. Combustion is often referred to as "burning."

compound: a chemical consisting of two or more elements chemically bonded together. Calcium atoms can combine with carbon atoms and oxygen atoms to make calcium carbonate, a compound of all three atoms.

condensation polymerization: where a water molecule is eliminated as every link in the polymer chain is formed.

cracking: breaking down complex molecules into simpler components. It is a term particularly used in oil refining.

crude oil: a chemical mixture of petroleum liquids. Crude oil forms the raw material for an oil refinery.

crystal: a substance that has grown freely so that it can develop external faces. Compare with crystalline, where the atoms were not free to form individual crystals, and amorphous, where the atoms are arranged irregularly.

dehydration: the removal of water from a substance by heating it, placing it in a dry atmosphere or using a drying agent.

electrode: a conductor that forms one terminal of a cell.

ester: organic compounds formed by the reaction of an alcohol with an acid and which often have a fruity taste.

extrusion: forming a shape by pushing it through a die. For example, toothpaste is extruded through the cap (die) of the toothpaste tube.

fossil fuels: hydrocarbon compounds that have been formed from buried plant and animal remains. High pressures and temperatures lasting over millions of years are required. The fossil fuels are coal, oil and natural gas.

fraction: a group of similar components of a mixture. In the petroleum industry the light fractions of crude oil are those with the smallest molecules, while the medium and heavy fractions have larger molecules.

gelatinous: a term meaning made with water. Because a gelatinous precipitate is mostly water, it is of a similar density to water and will float or lie suspended in the liquid.

glucose: the most common of the natural sugars. It occurs as the polymer known as cellulose, the fiber in plants. Starch is also a form of glucose. The breakdown of glucose provides the energy that animals need for life.

Greenhouse Effect: an increase in the global air temperature as a result of heat released from burning fossil fuels being absorbed by carbon dioxide in the atmosphere.

halogen: one of a group of elements including chlorine, bromine, iodine and fluorine.

latex: (the Latin word for "liquid"): a suspension of small polymer particles in water. The rubber that flows from a rubber tree is a natural latex. Some synthetic polymers are made as latexes, allowing polymerization to take place in water.

mineral: a solid substance made of just one element or chemical compound. Calcite is a mineral because it consists only of calcium carbonate; halite is a mineral because it contains only sodium chloride; quartz is a mineral because it consists of only silicon dioxide.

mixture: a material that can be separated into two or more substances using physical means.

molecule: a group of two or more atoms held together by chemical bonds.

monomer: a building block of a larger chain molecule ("mono" means one, "mer" means part).

noncombustible: a substance that will not burn.

oxidation: a reaction in which the oxidizing agent removes electrons. (Note that oxidizing agents do not have to contain oxygen.)

oxidation/reduction: a reaction in which oxygen is gained/lost.

oxidize: the process of gaining oxygen. This can be part of a controlled chemical reaction, or it can be the result of exposing a substance to the air, where oxidation (a form of corrosion) will occur slowly, perhaps over months or years.

petroleum: a natural mixture of a range of gases, liquids and solids derived from the decomposed remains of plants and animals.

photosynthesis: the process by which plants use the energy of the Sun to make the compounds they need for life. In photosynthesis six molecules of carbon dioxide from the air combine with six molecules of water, forming one molecule of glucose (sugar) and releasing six molecules of oxygen back into the atmosphere.

plastic (material): a carbon-based material consisting of long chains (polymers) of simple molecules. The word plastic is commonly restricted to synthetic polymers.

plastic (property): a material is plastic if it can be made to change shape easily. Plastic materials will remain in the new shape. (Compare with elastic, a property whereby a material goes back to its original shape.)

polymer: a compound that is made of long chains by combining molecules (called monomers) as repeating units. ("Poly" means many, "mer" means part.)

polymerization: a chemical reaction in which large numbers of similar molecules arrange themselves into large molecules, usually long chains. This process usually happens when there is a suitable catalyst present. For example, ethylene reacts to form polyethylene in the presence of certain catalysts.

reagent: a starting material for a reaction.

solvent: the main substance in a solution (e.g., water in saltwater).

sublimation: the change of a substance from solid to gas, or vica versa, without going through a liquid phase.

synthetic: does not occur naturally but has to be manufactured.

thermoplastic: a plastic that will soften and can repeatedly be molded into shape on heating and will set into the molded shape as it cools.

vapor: the gaseous form of a substance that is normally a liquid. For example, water vapor is the gaseous form of liquid water.

vulcanization: forming cross-links between polymer chains to increase the strength of the whole polymer. Rubbers are vulcanized using sulfur when making tires and other strong materials.

Set Index